Millie Marotta's

Wild Savannah

First published in the United Kingdom in 2016 by
Batsford
1 Gower Street
London
WC1E 6HD

An imprint of Pavilion Books Group Ltd

ISBN: 9781849943284

A CIP catalogue record for this book is available from the
British Library.

20 19 18 17 16
10 9 8 7 6 5 4 3 2

Repro by Mission, Hong Kong
Printed by C.O.S. Printers Pte Ltd, Singapore

This book can be ordered direct from the publisher at the website:
www.pavilionbooks.com, or try your local bookshop.

Millie Marotta's

Wild Savannah

a colouring book adventure

BATSFORD

Introduction

Those of you who already own my previous books *Animal Kingdom* and *Tropical Wonderland*, or indeed both, will know that I am rather obsessed with the natural world. It made a huge and lasting impression on me as a young child, leaving me quite spellbound, and is now the focal point of my work. Sharing my passion for the natural world through my own drawings allows me to indulge in my two favourite things, and I am thrilled to bring you my third book, *Wild Savannah*.

Wild Savannah is a collection of illustrations of all kinds of wild and wonderful creatures from our planet's swaying grasslands. I think when most of us ponder the word 'savannah', images of African wildlife spring to mind – lions, elephants, zebra and antelope, which would, of course, be quite correct. But, lurking amongst the pages of this book you will also discover some creatures that you might not have been expecting to find. Kangaroos from the savannah region of Northern Australia, for example, and other unlikely candidates from the savannahs of South America and Asia. Savannahs are home to such a diverse range of wildlife and with this book I want to whisk you away to explore a world of creatures, not just those that you are probably quite familiar with, but also some perhaps less obvious inhabitants. In rather an indulgent way, I also wanted to satisfy my own curiosity and explore an area of the natural world that I find absolutely fascinating.

Watching colouring-in become a creative outlet for so many people has been quite remarkable. I have had tremendous feedback to my books, and it's incredible to see so many people enjoying my illustrations. I never cease to be amazed by how differently each person colours in and how diverse their approach and ideas are towards each page. Many people are sharing their images through social media, inspiring one another with encouraging words, and swapping colouring tips, techniques and ideas for colour palettes. Every single coloured page I have seen from the last two books has been utterly unique. Some people enjoy laying down large areas of colour, while others prefer to fill every tiny individual detail, and I see people using colours in fabulous combinations that I would never have thought of myself. However you choose to colour the illustrations in *Wild Savannah*, you will be turning the illustrations into distinctive artworks of your own.

Dotted throughout the book you will find a sprinkling of illustrations with areas that have been left empty, inviting you to fill them with your own intricate patterns and textures as well as colour. For those of you feeling even more adventurous, there are lots of opportunities to add to the illustrations by drawing in backgrounds or habitats to surround the creatures.

I'm often asked which materials I like to use myself and which are best to use in the books. My firm favourite will always be a good set of coloured pencils. This is my own personal preference — there is no right or wrong and it is up to you to choose whatever materials you enjoy working with. I simply find coloured pencils incredibly versatile as they allow for blending, shading and building up layers of colour. When choosing new pencils I always opt for vibrant colours and like to find a set that are soft enough for blending, but hard enough to be sharpened to a nice fine point for colouring all those tiny details.

The last few pages have been left blank for you. These can be handy as tester pages to try out new materials or you may choose to use them as doodle pages for practicing your drawings before you add to the main illustrations. If you are feeling rather bold you could even use them to create your own creatures and wild grasslands.

Whether you enjoy colouring as a great way to beat stress or as a step back to a more hands-on activity in this digital age, I hope that my illustrations inspire and encourage you to explore your own creative side. Overall, I hope that you will enjoy making this book unique and individual, flooding it with colour, and bringing to life your very own wild savannah.

Millie Marotta

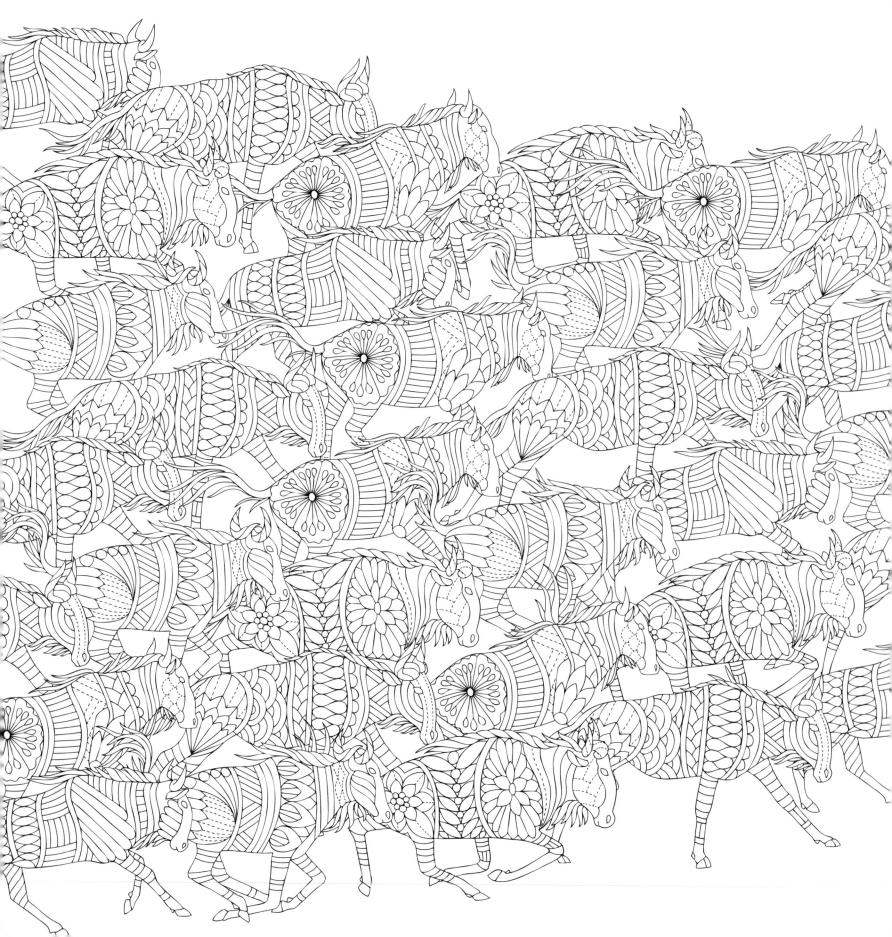

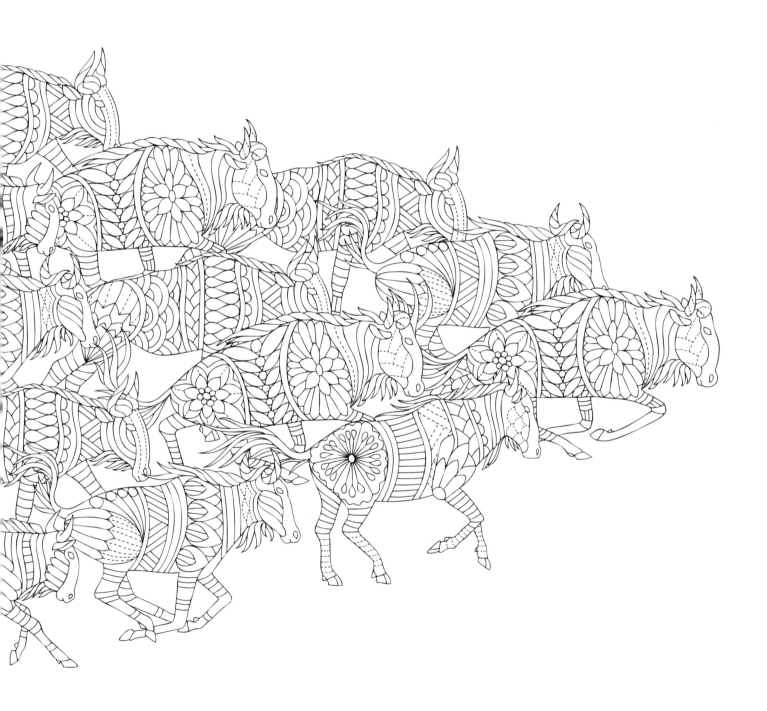

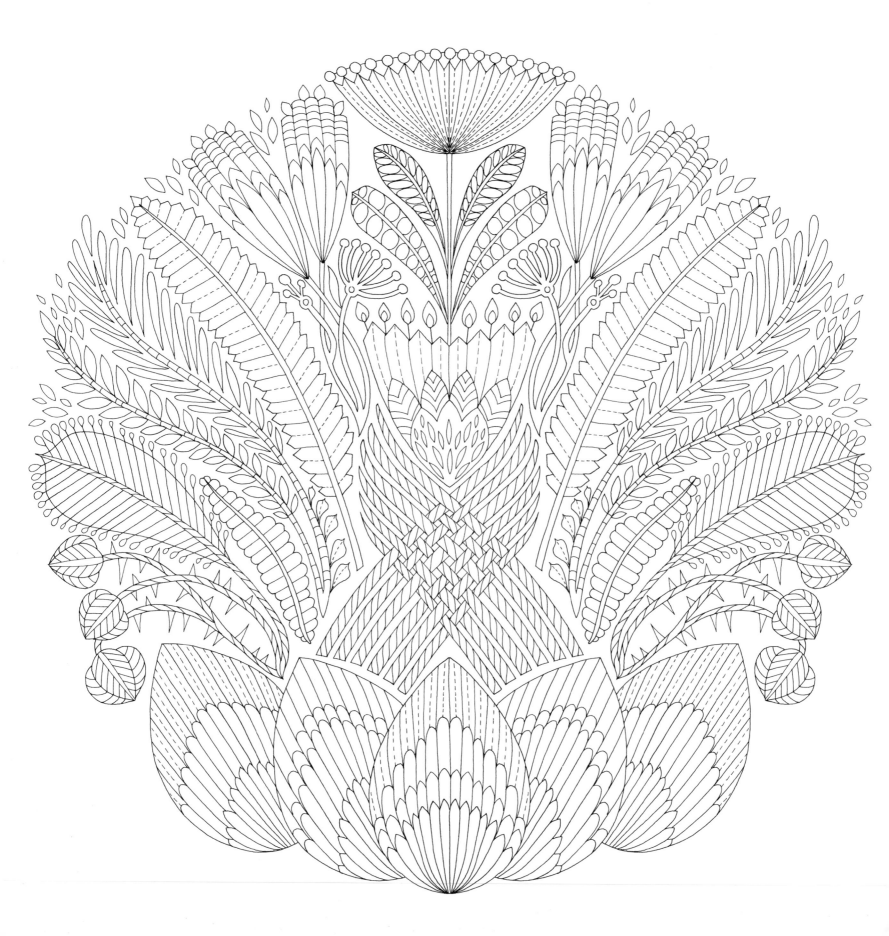

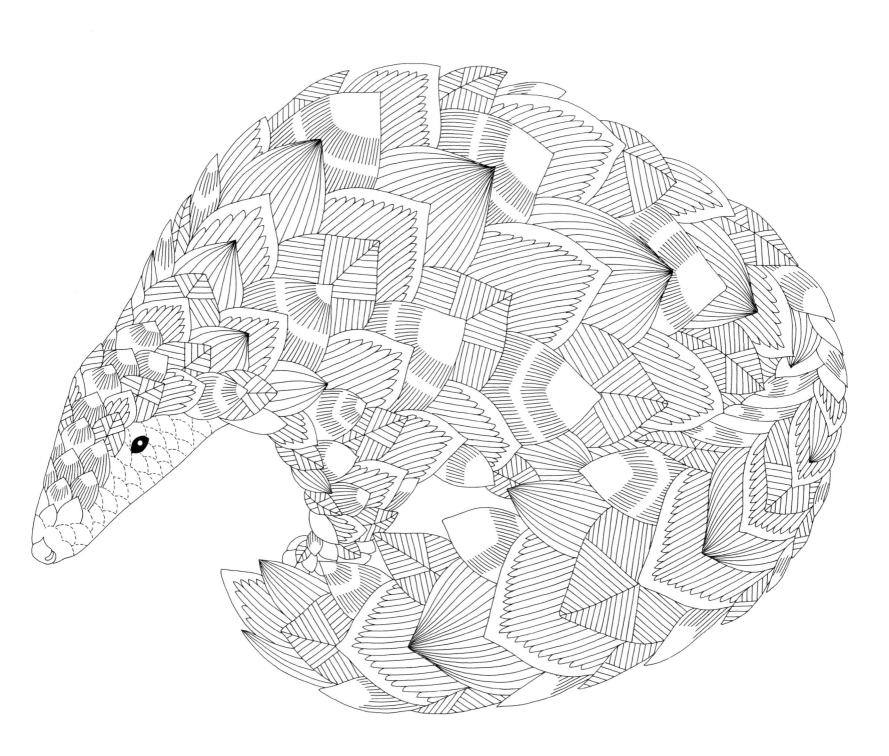

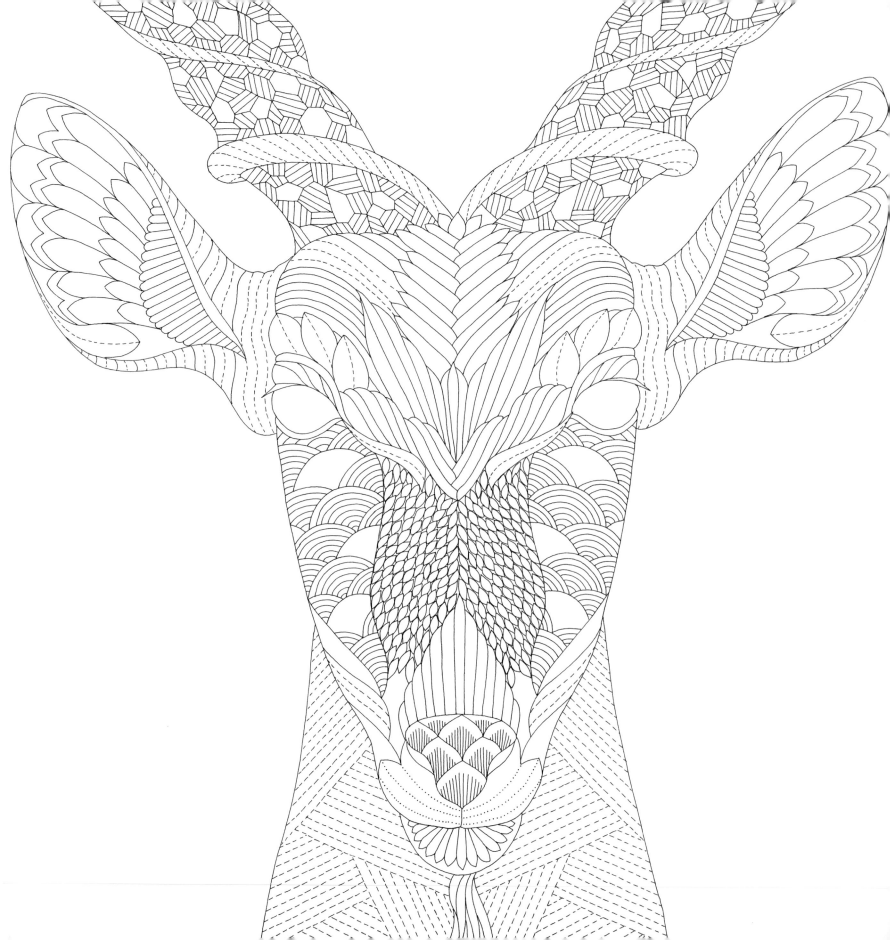

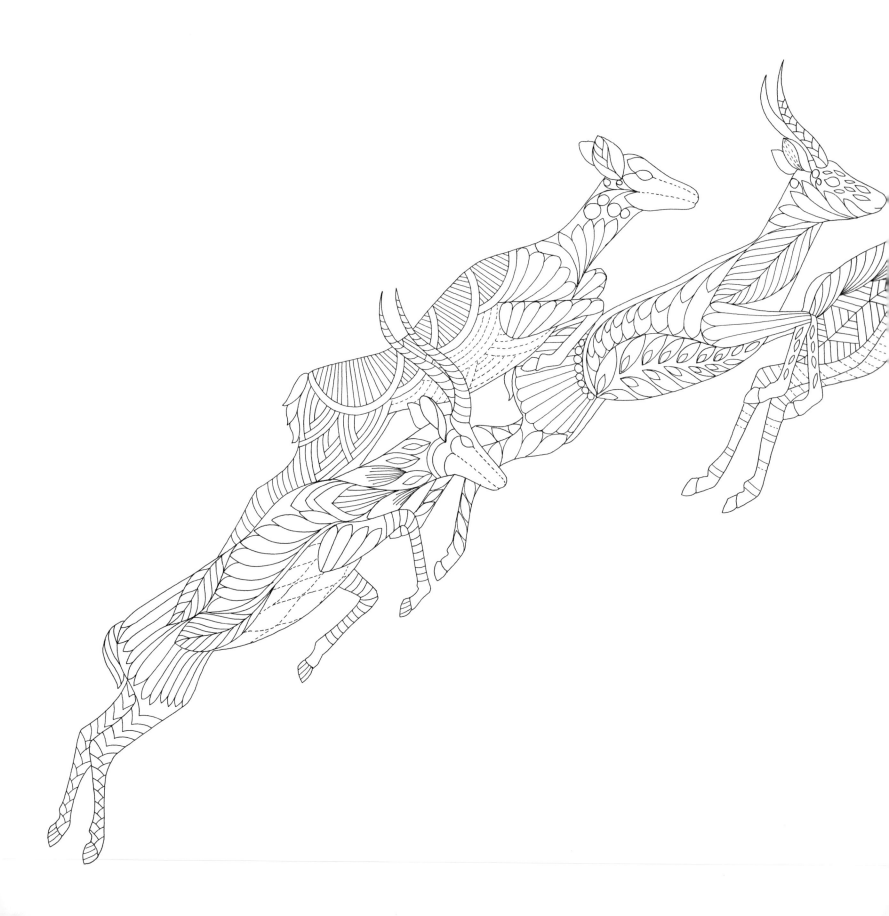

Create your own wild savannah here...